Groundworks

Algebraic Thinking
Grade 2

Carole Greenes
Carol Findell

Creative Publications®
A Tribune Education Company

Acknowledgments

Editors: Diane Nieker, Jeff Stiegel, Janet Pittock

Designer: Karen Lee

Production: Graphic Advantage, Ltd.

Illustrator: Susan Aiello Studio

Catalog Number 33378
Customer Service 800-624-0822
http://www.creativepublications.com

Printed in the United States of America.

ISBN: 0-7622-1206-3

2 3 4 5 6 7 8 / ML / 05 04 03 02 01 00 99

Contents

Why Teach Algebraic Thinking to Primary Students

Algebra for everyone is promoted by the National Council of Teachers of Mathematics (NCTM) in its Curriculum and Evaluation Standards (1999), by the College Board's Equity Project, and by authors of the Secretary's Commission on Achieving Necessary Skills (SCANS) Report (1991) on needs of the workplace. As a consequence, school districts around the country require all students to study algebra in high school. In some schools, students take formal algebra courses as early as early as the seventh, or even sixth, grade. Although students are capable of succeeding in algebra, often they do not.

Students who enter the study of algebra from an arithmetic-driven program often find the new content confusing and daunting. The main reason for this difficulty with algebra is a lack of preparation. Although the NCTM has recommended that students begin preparation for the big ideas of algebra during their elementary school years, current mathematics programs do not provide sufficient experiences. *Groundworks: Algebraic Thinking* introduces students to the six big ideas of algebra using interesting, challenging problems.

What *are* the Six Big Ideas of Algebra?

Groundworks: Algebraic Thinking develops understanding of the six big ideas of algebra:

Representation
Proportional Reasoning
Balance
Variable
Function
Inductive/Deductive Reasoning

Groundworks: Algebraic Thinking for grades 1–3 and *Algebra: Puzzles and Problems* for grades 4–7 provide challenging development of the six big ideas of algebra. In both series, problems build upon students' experiences with arithmetic reasoning and help them to make the connection between arithmetic and algebra. These early opportunities to make connections and to explore the big ideas of algebra enhance students' chances for success with algebra and with algebraic reasoning.

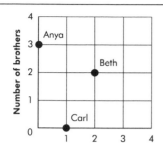

Representation

Representation is the display of mathematical relationships in diagrams, drawings, graphs, symbols, and tables. Students are asked to read, compare, and interpret information, and to explain their reasoning.

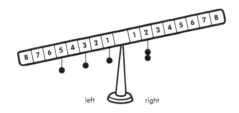

Proportional Reasoning

Proportional reasoning is determining how many objects from one group will be in a greater number of groups. Conversely, students may be asked to determine how may groups can be made from a certain number of objects. Students also use proportional reasoning when they make trades or compare prices.

Balance

Balance explores the concept of equality among variable expressions. Students develop understanding of equality and ways to modify inequalities to achieve balance or equality.

Variable

Understanding the meaning of variable is fundamental to algebra. Students grasp that the same shapes represent the same value, and different shapes represent different values.

Function

Students describe rules for relating inputs and outputs. They use the rule to predict outputs and to determine inputs.

Inductive and Deductive Reasoning

Students are asked to reason inductively by identifying patterns, and to extend these patterns. Deductive reasoning involves seeing a pattern emerge from other given information.

Design 1 **Design 2** **Design 3**

What Is in This Book?

Each book contains:

- general teacher information
- 15 blackline-master problems sets for students (a total of 90 pages of problems)
- teaching notes and solutions for the first page of each problem set
- solutions for all problems
- bibliography

Problem Sets

Each problem set consists of eight pages. The first page is a reproducible teaching problem. On the facing page, there is teacher information, including goals listing specific mathematical reasoning processes or skills, questions to ask students, and solutions. The next five pages are reproducible problem pages, each similar to the teaching problem page. Solutions are given on the eighth page of each problem set. For most problems, one solution method is shown; however, students may offer other valid methods. The mathematics required for the problems is in line with the generally approved mathematics curriculum for the grade level.

How to Use This Book

Have students work either individually or in pairs. Because many of the problem types will be new to your students, you may want to have the entire class or a large group of students work on the first problem in a set at the same time. You can use the questions that accompany the problem as the basis for a class discussion. As the students work on the problem, help them with difficulties they may encounter. Students are frequently asked to explain their thinking. You may choose to do this orally with the whole class. After students have several experiences telling about their thinking and hearing the thinking of others, they are usually better able to write about their own thinking. Once students have completed the first problem in a set, you may wish to assign the remaining problems for students to do on their own in school or for homework. If students have difficulty with the first problem in the set, you might do more of the problems with the whole class.

Although the big ideas and the families of problems within them come in a certain order, your students need not complete them in this order. Students might work the problem sets based on the mathematical content of the problems and their alignment with your curriculum, or according to student interests or needs.

At the Playground

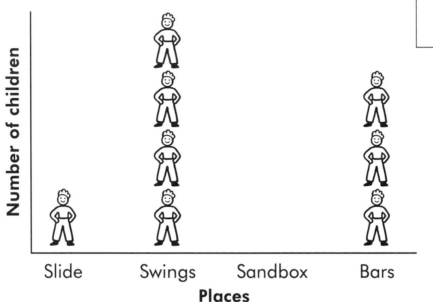

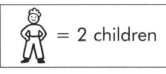 = 2 children

1 How many children are on the bars? _____ children

2 How many more children are on the slide than in the sandbox?

_____ children

3 How many fewer children are on the bars than on the swings?

_____ children

4 Write how you know. _____

_____

At the Playground

Solutions
p viii

Goals

Interpret a pictograph.

Match mathematical relationships presented in words with those shown in a pictograph.

Questions to Ask

What does the graph show? (where the children are in the playground)

What are the places where children play in the playground? (slide, swings, sandbox, bars)

What does one figure stand for? (2 children) ***How do you know?*** (legend in the box tells us)

How many figures are in the graph above "Bars"? (3) ***How many children do***
these figures represent? (2 + 2 + 2, or 6)

Solutions

1 6

2 2

3 2

4 Answers may vary. There is one fewer figure in the "Bars" column than in the "Swings" column. Each figure represents 2 children.

Notes

In this problem set, the legends create scales for each pictograph where one icon stands for more than one item. It may be helpful to ask a few questions about each pictograph to be sure that students understand the scale.

Library Books

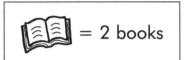 = 2 books

Type of book

Animals

Space

Rocks

People

Number of books

1 There are _____ books about space.

2 There are 10 books about _____.

3 There are 2 more books about people than about _____.

4 There are 4 more books about _____ than about rocks.

Dimitri's Hat Store

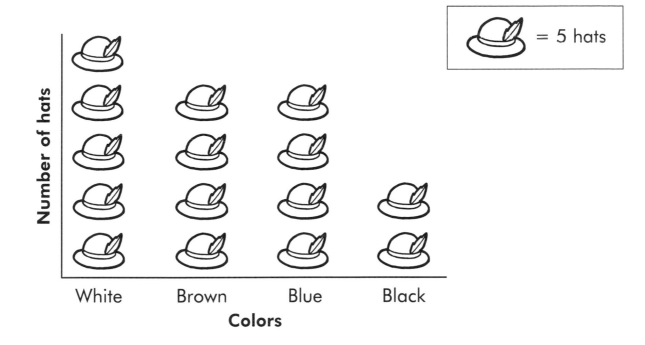

 = 5 hats

1 Dimitri has _____ blue hats.

2 Dimitri has 10 _____ hats.

3 Dimitri has the same number of _____ hats as _____ hats.

4 Dimitri has 5 fewer blue hats than _____ hats.

REPRESENTATION • PICTOGRAPH

Cans of Food

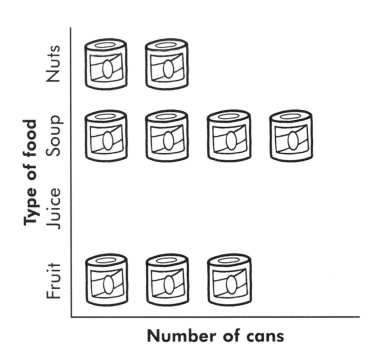

 = 2 cans

1 There are two more cans of _____ than of nuts.

2 There are 6 cans of _____.

3 There are _____ cans of juice.

4 There are half as many cans of _____ as of

_____.

Favorite Juices

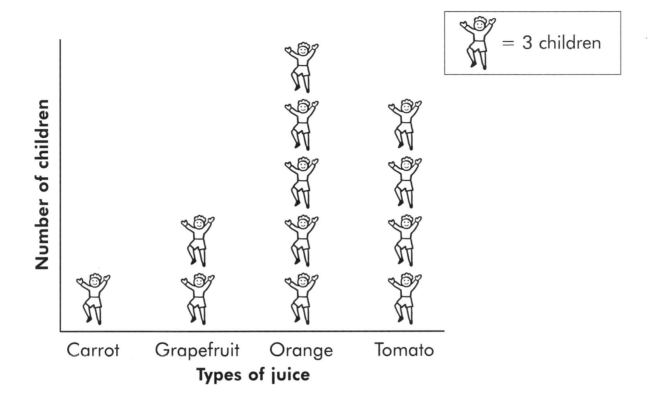

= 3 children

1 Carrot juice is the favorite of _____ children.

2 What is the favorite juice of the most children? _____

How many children like that juice? _____ children

3 How many more children like tomato juice than grapefruit juice?

_____ children

4 How can you tell from the graph? _____

_____

REPRESENTATION • PICTOGRAPH

Jars of Paint

= 4 jars

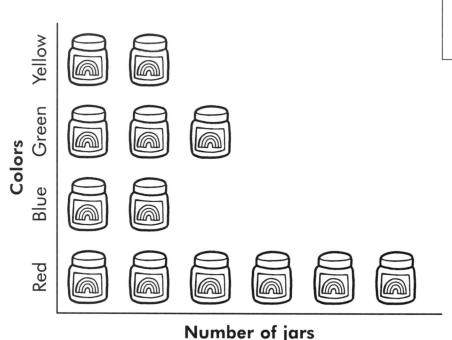

Colors

Yellow | Green | Blue | Red

Number of jars

1 There are _____ jars of yellow paint.

2 There are 4 more jars of _____ paint than blue paint.

3 How many fewer jars of green paint are there than red paint?

_____ jars

4 Write how you know. _____

_____

SOLUTIONS • Representation • Pictograph

Solutions
pp 2–6

Library Books

1 16

2 rocks

3 space

4 animals

Dimitri's Hat Store

1 20

2 black

3 brown, blue

4 white

Cans of Food

1 fruit

2 fruit

3 0

4 nuts, soup

Favorite Juices

1 3

2 orange, 15

3 6

4 Answers may vary. There are two more figures in the "Tomato" column than in the "Grapefruit" column. Each figure represents 3 children, and $3 + 3 = 6$.

Jars of Paint

1 8

2 green

3 12

4 Answers may vary. There are 3 fewer jars in the "Green" column than in the "Red" column. Each jar stands for 4 jars of paint, and $4 + 4 + 4 = 12$.

Blocks

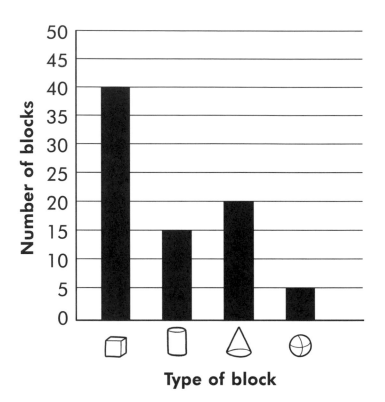

Shape		Number
Cube		40
Cylinder		15
Cone		20
Sphere		5

1 There are more _____ than any other block.

2 How can you tell from the graph? _____

3 How can you tell from the table? _____

4 There are 10 more cylinders than _____.

Blocks

Goals

Interpret a table.

Interpret a bar graph.

Complete a table to match data shown in a bar graph.

Match mathematical relationships presented in words with those shown in a graph and a table.

Questions to Ask

What shapes are shown in the table and graph? (cube, cylinder, cone, sphere)

From the table, there are the fewest number of which shape block? (sphere) *How can you tell?*

(It is the least number.)

How does the graph show that there are the fewest number of spheres?

(The "sphere" bar is the shortest.)

Solutions

1 cubes

2 "Cube" has the tallest bar in the graph.

3 "Cube" has the greatest number in the table.

4 spheres

Notes

In this problem set, information is delivered in two different formats, a bar graph and a table.

This gives students an opportunity see the same mathematical relationship in two formats.

Dan's Toys

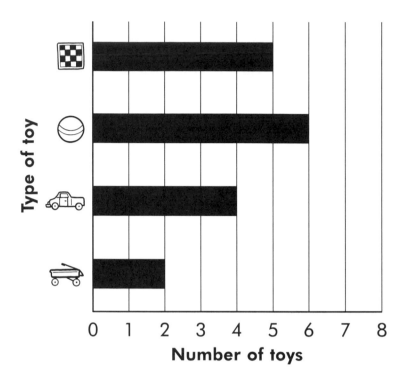

Toy		Number
Wagon	🛒	2
Truck	🚚	4
Ball	🔴	6
Game	▦	5

1 Dan has the most _____.

2 How can you tell from the graph? _____

3 How can you tell from the table? _____

_____

4 Dan has more games than _____ or

_____ .

Chalk Colors

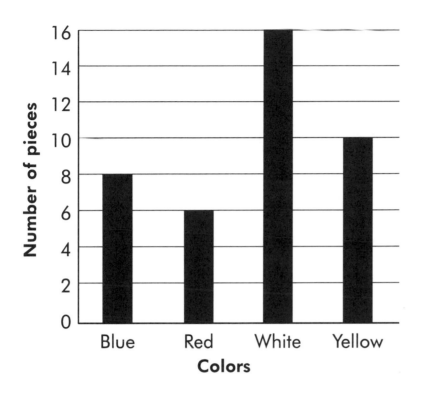

Color	Number
Blue	8
Red	6
White	16
Yellow	10

1 There are more pieces of blue chalk than _____ chalk.

2 There are fewer pieces of yellow chalk than _____ chalk.

3 There are twice as many pieces of white chalk as _____ chalk.

4 The total number of pieces of _____ chalk and

_____ chalk is 18.

REPRESENTATION • TABLES AND GRAPHS

Class Pets

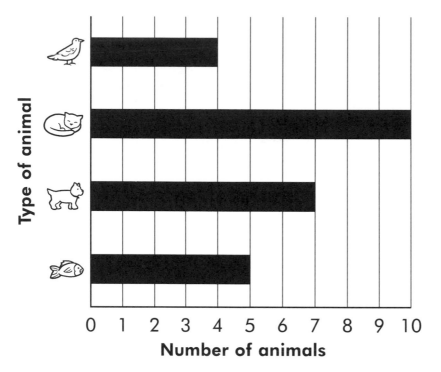

Animal	Number
Bird	4
	10
Dog	7
	5

1 Complete the table. Write the names of the animals.

2 There are _____ fish.

3 There are _____ more cats than dogs.

4 The total number of fish and birds is _____.

REPRESENTATION • TABLES AND GRAPHS

Stickers

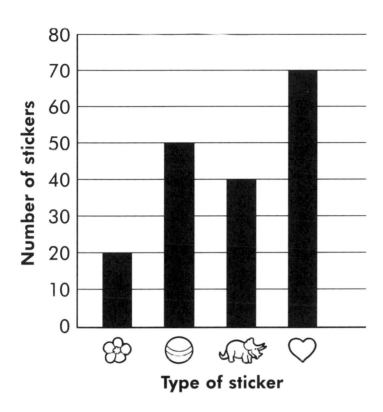

Sticker	Number
Flower	20
Ball	
Rhinoceros	
	70

1 Complete the table. Write the names and numbers of the stickers.

2 There are _____ heart stickers.

3 There are 10 more _____ than _____ stickers.

4 The total number of _____ and _____

stickers is 60.

REPRESENTATION • TABLES AND GRAPHS

Name

Sports Cards

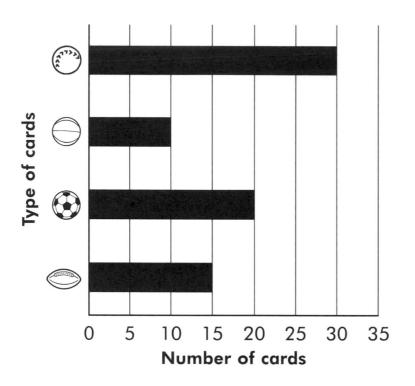

Type of cards

Number of cards: 0 5 10 15 20 25 30 35

Sport	Number
Baseball	
	10
Soccer	
	15

1 Compete the table. Write the names and numbers of cards.

2 There are _____ more football cards than basketball cards.

3 There are 20 more baseball cards than _____ cards.

4 The total number of cards is _____.

SOLUTIONS • Representation • Tables and Graphs

Solutions pp 10–14

Dan's Toys

1 balls

2 "Ball" has the longest bar in the graph.

3 "Ball" has the greatest number in the table.

4 wagons, trucks

Chalk Colors

1 red

2 white

3 blue

4 blue, yellow

Class Pets

1

Animal	Number
Bird	4
Cat	10
Dog	7
Fish	5

2 5

3 3

4 9

Stickers

1

Sticker	Number
Flower	20
Ball	50
Rhinoceros	40
Heart	70

2 70

3 ball, rhinoceros

4 flower, rhinoceros

Sports Cards

1

Sport	Number
Baseball	30
Basketball	10
Soccer	20
Football	15

2 5

3 basketball

4 75

Jackets and Backpacks

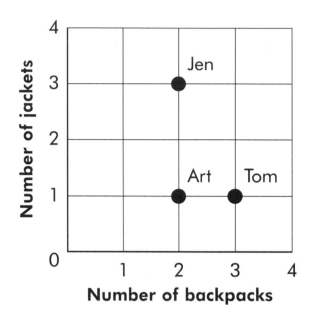

1 Who has the most jackets?_____

How many? _____ jackets

2 Who has the most backpacks?_____

How many? _____ backpacks

3 Who has 2 backpacks and 1 jacket? _____.

4 Art has 2 fewer jackets than _____.

5 _____ and _____ have the same

number of backpacks.

© CREATIVE PUBLICATIONS • 33378

Jackets and Backpacks

Solution
p 16

Goals

Interpret a scatter plot.

Match mathematical relationships given in words with those shown in a graph.

Make inferences.

Questions to Ask

What does each point on the graph represent? (Each point represents the number of backpacks and jackets for each child.)

What do the numbers along the bottom of the graph show? (number of backpacks)

What do the numbers along the side of the graph show? (number of jackets)

How many backpacks does Art have? (2 backpacks)

How many jackets does Art have? (1 jacket)

Solutions

1 Jen, 3

2 Tom, 3

3 Art

4 Jen

5 Jen and Art

Notes

In this problem set, each scatter plot shows information about three different people. Each person is represented by a dot on the scatter plot. That dot gives two pieces of information, one recorded on the horizontal scale, the other on the vertical scale.

REPRESENTATION • WHO IS IT?

Pencils and Crayons

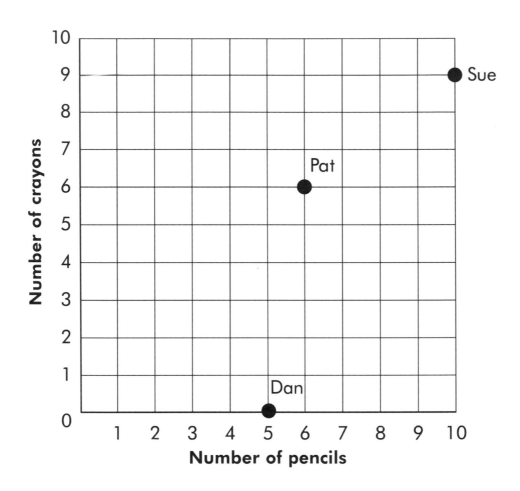

1 Who has no crayons? _____

2 Who has the same number of pencils as crayons? _____

3 Who has the most pencils? _____

4 Who has the most crayons? _____

5 Who has 1 more pencil than Dan? _____

Stickers and Books

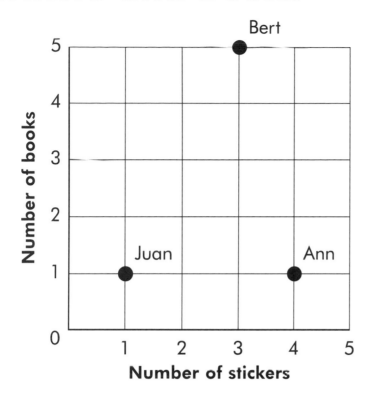

1 Who has the most books? _____

2 Who has the most stickers? _____

How many stickers? _____

3 Who has the same number of books and stickers? _____

4 Who has 1 more sticker than Bert? _____

5 Who as 4 fewer books than Bert? _____

Brothers and Sisters

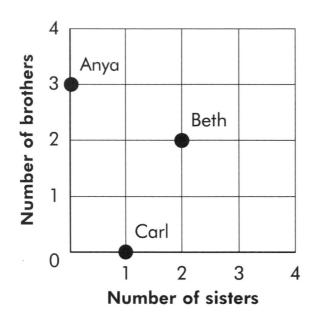

1 Who has no brothers? _____

2 How many sisters does Anya have? _____

3 Who has the same number of brothers as sisters? _____

4 How many children are there in Anya's family? _____

5 Who has 3 more brothers than sisters? _____

Puzzles and Games

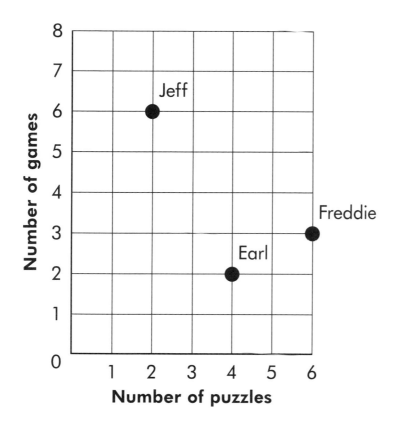

1 Who has 6 games? _____

2 How many puzzles does Earl have? _____

3 _____ has 3 more games than Freddie.

4 Jeff and Freddie have how many puzzles all together? _____

5 Who has the most puzzles and games all together? _____

REPRESENTATION • WHO IS IT?

T-Shirts and Caps

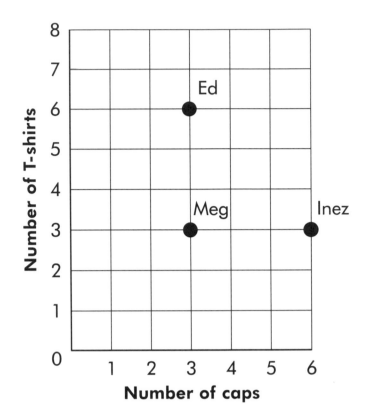

1 Who has twice as many T-shirts as Inez? _____

2 _____ and _____ have the same number

of caps.

3 _____ and _____ have the same number

of T-shirts.

4 _____ has 3 more T-shirts than caps.

5 _____ has more caps than T-shirts.

SOLUTIONS • Representation • Who Is It?

Solutions
pp 18–22

Pencils and Crayons

1 Dan

2 Pat

3 Sue

4 Sue

5 Pat

Puzzles and Games

1 Jeff

2 4

3 Jeff

4 8

5 Freddie

Stickers and Books

1 Bert

2 Ann, 4

3 Juan

4 Ann

5 Juan, Ann

T-Shirts and Caps

1 Ed

2 Meg, Ed

3 Meg, Inez

4 Ed

5 Inez

Brothers and Sisters

1 Carl

2 none

3 Beth

4 4

5 Anya

Baskets 1

Each lunch basket has:

1 sandwich   3 carrots   2 cookies   1 apple

Make 3 lunch baskets.

You need:

1 _____ sandwiches

2 _____ carrots

3 How many lunch baskets can you make with 10 cookies?

_____ lunch baskets

4 How many apples would you need? _____ apples

5 Explain how you know. _____

_____

▲▲▲▲▲▲▲▲▲▲▲▲▲▲▲▲▲▲▲▲▲▲▲▲

Baskets 1

Solutions
p 24

Goals

Create matching sets.

Identify multiples of numbers of objects in a set.

Questions to Ask

What is in each lunch basket? (1 sandwich, 3 carrots, 2 cookies, and 1 apple)

How many carrots will you need to make 2 lunch baskets? (6 carrots) ***How did you know?***

   (Students may draw the carrots in each basket or recognize that two 3's, 3 + 3, is 6.)

If you have 8 cookies, what is the greatest number of baskets you could fill with 2 cookies in each

   basket? (4 baskets) ***How did you know?*** (Each basket has to have 2 cookies, and four 2's is 8.)

Solutions

1 3

2 9

3 5

4 5

5 Answers may vary. Students might mark or group items that belong in the same basket and then
count the groups, or they may test each quantity to determine the number of baskets. 10 cookies,
2 per basket, will make 5 baskets; one apple per basket, to make 5 baskets, requires 5 apples.

Notes

In this problem set, students deal with basic multiplication concepts and proportional reasoning.
You may wish to make extra paper available for students who need to sketch the baskets.

Baskets 2

Each fruit basket has:

2 bananas   4 apples   5 pears

Make 2 fruit baskets.

You need:

1 _____ bananas

2 _____ pears

3 How many fruit baskets can you make with 12 apples?

_____ fruit baskets

4 How many pears would you need? _____ pears

5 Explain how you know. _____

_____

Baskets 3

Each fruit basket has:

1 banana   2 grapefruit   3 plums

Make 4 fruit baskets.

You need:

1 _____ bananas

2 _____ plums

3 How many fruit baskets can you make with 12 grapefruit?

_____ fruit baskets

4 How many bananas would you need?_____ bananas

5 Explain how you know. _____

_____

Baskets 4

Each lunch basket has:

1 juice box   2 sandwiches   4 carrots

Make 3 lunch baskets.

You need:

1 _____ sandwiches

2 _____ carrots

3 _____ juice boxes

4 To make _____ lunch baskets, you need

_____ juice boxes, 8 sandwiches, and 16 carrots.

5 Explain how you know. _____

_____

Baskets 5

Each lunch basket has:

      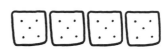

1 water   2 sandwiches   3 carrots   4 crackers

Make 5 lunch baskets.

You need:

1 _____ sandwiches

2 _____ carrots

3 _____ crackers

4 _____ bottles of water

5 To make _____ lunch baskets you need

_____ bottles of water, _____ sandwiches,

30 carrots, and 40 crackers.

PROPORTIONAL REASONING • BASKETS

Baskets 6

Each fruit basket has

2 bunches of grapes   2 bananas   3 peaches   2 pineapples

Make 3 fruit baskets.

You need:

1 _____ bunches of grapes, _____ bananas,

_____ peaches, and _____ pineapples

2 How many fruit baskets can you make with 8 bananas?

_____ fruit baskets

3 How many peaches would you need? _____ peaches

4 You have 6 bunches of grapes, 6 bananas, 6 pineapples, and

6 peaches. How many full baskets can you make? _____

5 Explain how you know. _____

_____

▲ ▲

SOLUTIONS • Proportional Reasoning • Baskets

Solutions
pp 26–30

Baskets 2

1 4

2 10

3 3

4 15

5 Answers may vary. 12 apples, 4 per basket, will make 3 baskets; 5 pears in each of 3 baskets requires 15 pears.

Baskets 3

1 4

2 12

3 6

4 6

5 Answers may vary. 12 grapefruit, 2 per basket, will make 6 baskets; 1 banana in each of 6 baskets requires 6 bananas.

Baskets 4

1 6

2 12

3 3

4 4, 4

5 Answers may vary. Eight sandwiches are needed for 4 baskets; 16 carrots are needed for 4 baskets. Thus the number of baskets is 4 and the number of juice boxes is 1 + 1 + 1 + 1, or 4.

Baskets 5

1 10

2 15

3 20

4 5

5 10, 10, 20

Baskets 6

1 6, 6, 9, 6

2 4

3 12

4 2

5 Answers may vary. Since there are enough bunches of grapes for 3 fruit baskets, enough bananas for 3 fruit baskets, enough peaches for 2 fruit baskets, and enough pineapples for 3 fruit baskets, you can fill only 2 fruit baskets.

PROPORTIONAL REASONING • BASKETS

Crayons

There are 4 crayons in one box.

1 3 boxes hold _____ crayons.

2 _____ boxes hold 16 crayons.

3 Which is more crayons: 6 boxes of crayons or 20 crayons?

_____ crayons

4 Write how you know. _____

_____

_____

Crayons

Solutions
p 32

Goals

Create matching sets.

Identify multiples of numbers of objects in a set.

Questions to Ask

How many crayons are in each box? (4 crayons)

How many crayons are there in 2 boxes? (8 crayons)

If you had 28 crayons, how many boxes would you need? (7 boxes) *How could you figure it out?*
   (Draw 28 crayons, ring groups of 4, and count the rings; or add 4's until the sum is 28 and
   count the number of 4's added.)

Solutions

1 12

2 4

3 6 boxes

4 6 boxes is 6 groups of 4 crayons; 6 x 4 is 24 and 24 is greater than 20.

Notes

In this problem set, students deal with basic multiplication concepts and proportional reasoning. You
may want to make extra paper available for students who need more space to sketch the containers.

Erasers

There are 2 erasers in one box.

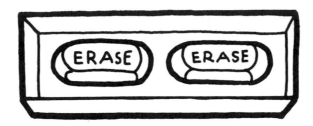

1 _____ boxes hold 6 erasers.

2 5 boxes hold _____ erasers.

3 Which is more erasers: 6 boxes of erasers or 10 erasers?

_____ erasers

4 Write how you know. _____

_____

_____

Tennis Balls

One can holds 3 tennis balls.

1 2 cans hold _____ tennis balls.

2 _____ cans hold 12 tennis balls.

3 Which is more tennis balls: 5 cans of tennis balls or 14 tennis balls?

_____ tennis balls

4 Write how you know. _____

_____

_____

Pencils

There are 5 pencils in one box.

1 3 boxes hold _____ pencils.

2 _____ boxes hold 10 pencils.

3 Which is more pencils: 4 boxes of pencils or 22 pencils?

_____ pencils

4 Write how you know. _____

_____

_____

PROPORTIONAL REASONING • CONTAINERS

Bagels

One bag holds 6 bagels.

1 How many bagels are in 3 bags? _____ bagels

2 _____ bags hold 12 bagels.

3 Which is fewer bagels? 5 bags of bagels or 24 bagels?

_____ bagels

4 How do you know? _____

_____

_____

Tacks

One package holds 10 tacks.

1 How many tacks are in 4 packages? _____ tacks

2 _____ packages hold 30 tacks.

3 Which is fewer? 5 packages of tacks or 60 tacks?

_____ tacks

4 How do you know? _____

_____

_____

SOLUTIONS • Proportional Reasoning • Containers

Solutions
pp 34–38

Erasers

1 3

2 10

3 6 boxes

4 6 boxes is 6 groups of 2 erasers; six 2's is 12 and 12 is greater than 10.

Bagels

1 18

2 2

3 24 bagels

4 5 bags of bagels is 5 groups of 6 bagels; five 6's is 30 and 24 is less than 30.

Tennis Balls

1 6

2 4

3 5 cans

4 5 cans is 5 groups of 3 tennis balls; five 3's is 15 and 15 is greater than 14.

Tacks

1 40

2 3

3 5 packages

4 5 packages is 5 groups of 10 tacks; five 10's is 50 and 50 is less than 60.

Pencils

1 15

2 2

3 22 pencils

4 4 boxes of pencils is 4 groups of 5 pencils; four 5's is 20 and 20 is less than 22.

Shapes for Shapes 1

Trade  △ △ for ▱.

1 _____ △ for ▱.

_____ △ for ▱ ▱ ▱.

2 _____ ▱ for △ △ △ △.

_____ ▱ for △ △ △ △ △ △ △ △.

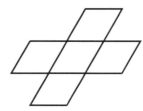

Design A

3 _____ ▱ for Design A.

_____ △ for Design A.

Design B

4 _____ ▱ for Design B.

_____ △ for Design B.

PROPORTIONAL REASONING • SHAPES FOR SHAPES

Shapes for Shapes 1

Solutions
p 40

Goals

Trade for equal amounts.

Identify multiples of numbers of shapes.

Recognize area and volume equivalencies.

Questions to Ask

What are the names of the shapes that you can trade? (triangle, rhombus)

How many triangles do you have to trade to get one rhombus? (2 triangles) *How many rhombuses do you have to trade to get two triangles?* (1 rhombus)

How many triangles are there in the first trade in question 2? (4 triangles) *How can you figure out the number of rhombuses you should trade for the 4 triangles?* (One rhombus is equivalent to 2 triangles. There are 2 groups of 2 triangles so 2 rhombuses should be traded for the 4 triangles.)

Solutions

1 2, 6

2 2, 4

3 5, 10

4 7, 14

Notes

In this problem set, designs are made of shapes that can be replaced with other shapes, preserving the area and volume. Some designs picture pattern blocks and others picture geoblocks cubes and prisms. Making patterns and constructions with pattern blocks and geoblocks, it provides a nice concrete-to-representational connection.

Shapes for Shapes 2

Trade ☐☐☐☐ for ☐ .

1 _____ ☐ for ☐ .

_____ ☐ for ☐☐ .

2 _____ ☐ for ☐☐☐
☐☐☐ .

_____ ☐ for ☐☐☐
☐☐☐
☐☐☐
☐☐☐ .

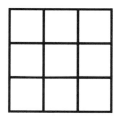

Design A

3 _____ ☐ for Design A.

4 _____ ☐ for Design A.

PROPORTIONAL REASONING • SHAPES FOR SHAPES

Shapes for Shapes 3

Trade △ △ △ for ⬜.

1 _____ △ for ⬜.

_____ △ for ⬜ ⬜ ⬜.

2 _____ ⬜ for △ △ △ △ △ △.

_____ ⬜ for ◇ ◇ ◇ ◇ ◇ ◇.

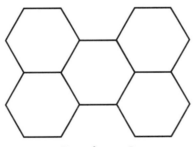

Design A

3 _____ ⬜ for Design A.

4 _____ △ for Design A.

Shapes for Shapes 4

Trade  for .

1 _____ for .

_____ for .

2 _____ for .

_____ for .

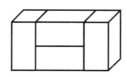

Design A

3 _____ for Design A.

_____ for Design A.

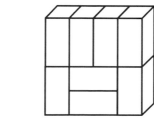

Design B

4 _____ for Design B.

_____ for Design B.

PROPORTIONAL REASONING • SHAPES FOR SHAPES

Shapes for Shapes 5

Trade ⬜⬜⬜ for ▱.

1 _____ ⬜ for ▱.

_____ ⬜ for ▭.

2 _____ ▱ for ⬜⬜⬜⬜⬜⬜.

_____ ▱ for .

3 _____ ▱ for Design A.

_____ ⬜ for Design A.

Design A

4 _____ ▱ for Design B.

_____ ⬜ for Design B.

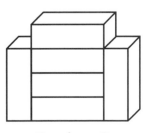

Design B

Shapes for Shapes 6

Trade 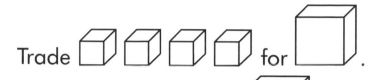 for .

1 _____  for .

_____  for .

2 _____  for .

_____ for .

3 _____ for Design A.

_____ for Design A.

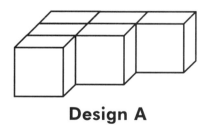

Design A

4 _____ for Design B.

_____ for Design B.

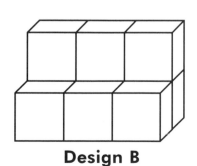

Design B

△ △

SOLUTIONS • Proportional Reasoning • Shapes for Shapes

Solutions
pp 42–46

Shapes for Shapes 2

1 4, 8

2 2, 4

3 9

4 36

Shapes for Shapes 3

1 3, 9

2 2, 4

3 10

4 30

Shapes for Shapes 4

1 2, 4

2 4, 8

3 4, 8

4 8, 16

Shapes for Shapes 5

1 3, 6

2 2, 6

3 4, 12

4 6, 18

Shapes for Shapes 6

1 4, 8

2 3, 12

3 6, 24

4 9, 36

On the Level 1

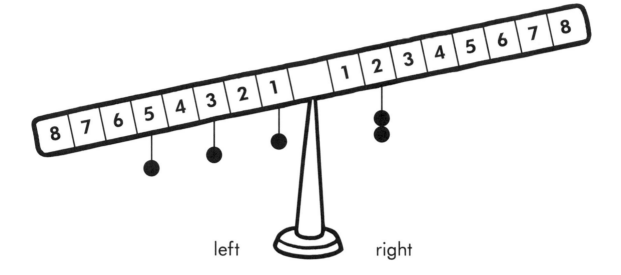

left   right

Make the number balance level.

Draw one ● on the right side.

1 Hang the ● from number _____ .

2 Write how you know. _____

_____

_____

On the Level 1

Solutions p 48

Goals

Recognize that a level balance represents equality.

Recognize that balance is achieved when the sum of numbers on each side of the balance is the same.

Recognize that the lower side of the beam shows the greater sum.

Questions to Ask

Which side of the number balance is heavier? (left side)

On the left side, which numbers are the balls hanging from? (5, 3, and 1) *What is the sum?* (9)

On the right side, which number are the balls hanging from? (2) *What is the sum?* (4)

Solutions

1   5

2   The left side is 9. Add a ball to 5 on the right side to get a sum of 9. $5 + 3 + 1 = 2 + 2 + 5$

Notes

In this problem set, a number balance is pictured. Each ball weighs the same amount and "pulls down" a value equal to the number it hangs from on the beam. For example, a ball at 4 on one side balances balls hanging from 1 and 3 on the other side. A ball at 4 on one side also balances two balls hanging from 2 on the other side. If possible, allow students to experiment with a real number balance.

On the Level 2

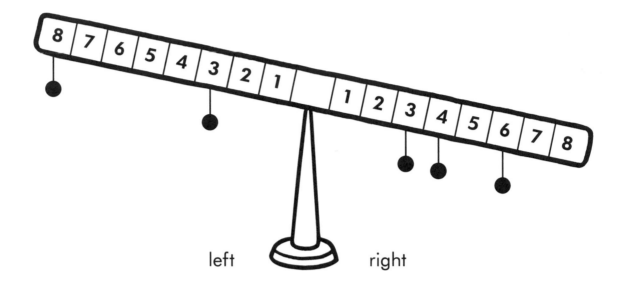

left   right

Make the number balance level.

Draw one ● on the left side.

1 Hang the ● from number _____.

2 Write how you know. _____

_____

_____

On the Level 3

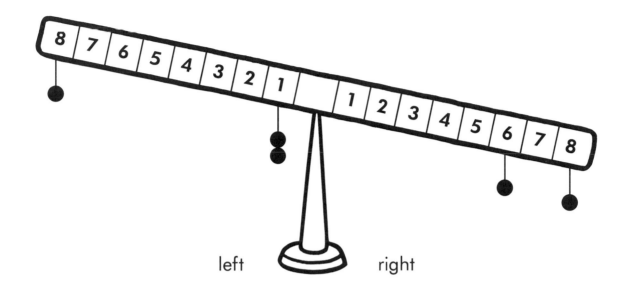

left   right

Make the number balance level.

Draw one ● on the left side.

1 Hang the ● from number _____.

2 Write how you know. _____

_____

_____

On the Level 4

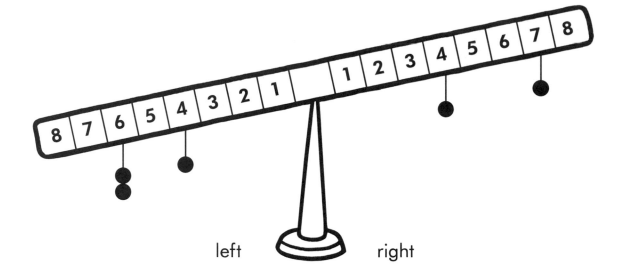

left   right

Make the number balance level.

Draw one ● on the right side.

1 Hang the ● from number _____ .

2 Write how you know. _____

_____

_____

On the Level 5

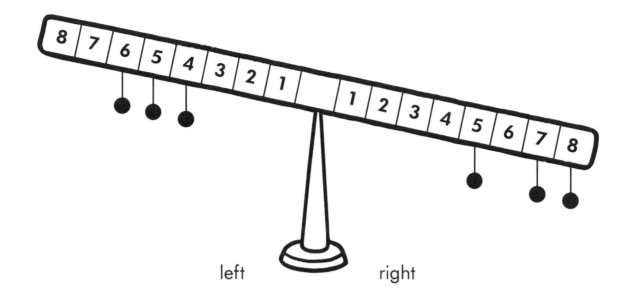

left   right

Make the number balance level.

Draw one 🔴 on the left side.

1 Hang the 🔴 from number _____ .

2 Write how you know. _____

_____

_____

On the Level 6

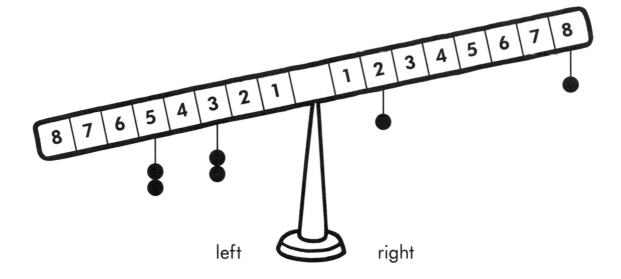

left   right

Make the number balance level.

Draw one ● on the right side.

1 Hang the ● from number _____.

2 Write how you know. _____

_____

_____

SOLUTIONS • Balance • On the Level

Solutions
pp 50–54

On the Level 2

1 2

2 The right side sum is 13. Add a ball to 2 on the left side to get a sum of 13. 8 + 3 + 2 = 3 + 4 + 6

On the Level 3

1 4

2 The right side sum is 14. Add a ball to 4 on the left side to get a sum of 14. 8 + 1 + 1 + 4 = 6 + 8

On the Level 4

1 5

2 The left side sum is 16. Add a ball to 5 on the right side to get a sum of 16. 6 + 6 + 4 = 4 + 7 + 5

On the Level 5

1 5

2 The right side sum is 20. Add a ball to 5 on the left side to get a sum of 20. 5 + 4 + 6 + 5 = 5 + 7 + 8

On the Level 6

1 6

2 The left side sum is 16. Add a ball to 6 on the right side to get a sum of 16. 5 + 5 + 3 + 3 = 2 + 8 + 6

Weighing In 1

1 Ring the block that weighs more.

2 Ring the block that weighs more.

3 Ring the block that weighs the most.

4 Write how you know. _____

_____

_____

Weighing In 1

Solutions
p 56

Goals

Deduce weight relationships from visual clues.

Recognize that a balanced two-pan scale represents equality.

Recognize that the lower pan on a two-pan scale holds the object(s) that weighs more.

Questions to Ask

Which pan scale is balanced? (A)

What can you say about the weights of the cube and the cylinder? (They are the same weight.)

Which block is heavier on Scale B? (sphere) *How can you tell?* (The scale is tipped to the right and the sphere is in the pan on the right side.)

Solutions

1 sphere

2 sphere

3 sphere

4 Since the sphere is heavier than the cube and the cube and cylinder weigh the same, the sphere is also heavier than the cylinder.

Notes

In this problem set, it is beneficial for students to have experience with a balance before they do the problems. Concrete experiences with balancing provide the groundwork for many equality and inequality concepts.

Weighing In 2

1 How many weigh the same as one ? _____

2 Ring the block that weighs the most.

3 Write how you know. _____

_____

4 Ring the block that weighs the least.

5 Write how you know. _____

_____

Weighing In 3

1 Ring the block that weighs more.

2 Ring the block that weighs more.

3 Ring the block that weighs the least.

4 Write how you know. _____

_____

_____

Weighing In 4

1 Ring the block that weighs more.

2 Ring the block that weighs less.

3 Ring the block that weighs the most.

4 Write how you know. _____

_____

_____

Weighing In 5

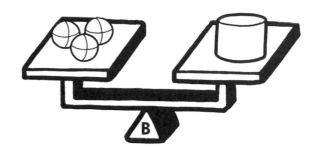

1 How many weigh the same as one ? _____

2 Ring the block that weighs the most.

3 Write how you know. _____

_____

4 Ring the block that weighs the least.

5 Write how you know. _____

_____

Weighing In 6

1 Ring the block that weighs more.

2 Ring the block that weighs less.

3 Ring the block that weighs the most.

4 Write how you know. _____

_____

SOLUTIONS • Balance • Weighing In

Solutions
pp 58–62

Weighing In 2

1 2

2 cube

3 On Scale B, one cylinder balances 2 spheres. So the cylinder is heavier than the sphere. On Scale A, one cube balances 2 cylinders, so the cube is heavier than the cylinder. Therefore, it's heavier than the spheres, too.

4 sphere

5 Following the reasoning for question 3, the sphere weighs the least.

Weighing In 3

1 sphere

2 cube

3 cylinder

4 On Scale B, one cube balances 2 spheres, thus the cube is heavier than the sphere. Since the sphere is heavier than 3 cylinders on Scale A, it must be heavier than one cylinder. The order of blocks from heaviest to lightest is cube, sphere, cylinder.

Weighing In 4

1 cube

2 sphere

3 cube

4 The cube balances 3 spheres and the cylinder balances 2 spheres. Thus, the cube weighs more than the cylinder. The sphere weighs the least.

Weighing In 5

1 4

2 cube

3 On Scale A, 2 cubes balance 8 spheres, so one cube balances 4 spheres. On Scale B, one cylinder balances 3 spheres. Thus, the cube is heaviest.

4 sphere

5 Since 4 spheres balances one cube and 3 spheres balances one cylinder, the sphere must weigh the least.

Weighing In 6

1 sphere

2 sphere

3 cylinder

4 On Scale A, the sphere is heavier than the cube. On Scale B, the cylinder is heavier than the sphere. Thus, the cylinder is heaviest.

Mystery Numbers 1

Same shapes are same numbers.

$$\square + \square = 12 \qquad \square + \triangle + \triangle = 20$$

1 What number is $\square$? _____

2 What number is $\triangle$? _____

3 Explain how you found the numbers. _____

_____

_____

Solutions
p 64

Mystery Numbers 1

Goals

Replace variables with numbers in equations.

Identify relationships between variables and numbers.

Questions to Ask

What do the squares and triangles stand for? (numbers)

What does the equal sign (=) mean? (The sum of the numbers on the left side of the equal sign is 12.)

What number in the squares will make the first example true? (6)

How do you know? (Because 6 + 6 = 12.)

In the second example, if the square is 6, what number is the triangle? (7)

Solutions

1 6

2 7

3 Answers will vary. Since square plus square is 12 in the first example, and the double 6 + 6 is 12, the square must be 6. That means that, in the second example, 6 plus triangle plus triangle is 20, so triangle plus triangle is 20 – 6, or 14. Since the double 7 + 7 is 14, then triangle must be 7.

Notes

In this problem set, students need to know that each shape stands for the same number wherever it appears. Once they know that, they can use their understanding of addition and subtraction to solve the problems.

Mystery Numbers 2

Same shapes are same numbers.

$$\triangle + \triangle = 10 \qquad \square + \triangle = 8$$

1 What number is $\triangle$? _____

2 What number is $\square$? _____

3 Explain how you found the numbers. _____

_____

_____

Mystery Numbers 3

Same shapes are same numbers.

$$\triangle + \triangle + \triangle = 6 \qquad \square + \triangle = 10$$

1 What number is $\triangle$? _____

2 What number is $\square$? _____

3 Explain how you found the numbers. _____

_____

_____

Mystery Numbers 4

Same shapes are same numbers.

$$\square + \triangle = 5 \qquad \triangle + \triangle + 2 = 10$$

1 What number is $\triangle$? _____

2 What number is $\square$? _____

3 Explain how you found the numbers. _____

_____

_____

Mystery Numbers 5

Same shapes are same numbers.

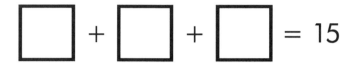 $+$ $+$ $= 15$ $\triangle - \square = \square$

1 What is $\square$? _____

2 What is $\triangle$? _____

3 Explain how you found the numbers. _____

_____

_____

VARIABLE • MYSTERY NUMBERS

★ ★ ★ ★ ★ ★

Mystery Numbers 6

Same shapes are same numbers.

$$\square + \triangle + \triangle = 22 \qquad \square + \triangle = 13$$

1 What is $\triangle$? _____

2 What is $\square$? _____

3 Explain how you found the numbers. _____

_____

_____

© CREATIVE PUBLICATIONS • **33378**

Solutions
pp 66–70

SOLUTIONS • Variable • Mystery Numbers

Mystery Numbers 2

1 5

2 3

3 Answers will vary. In the first example, triangle plus triangle is 10. Since the double 5 + 5 is 10, triangle must be 5. In the second example, then, square plus 5 is 8, so square is 8 – 5, or 3.

Mystery Numbers 3

1 2

2 8

3 Answers will vary. In the first example, triangle plus triangle plus triangle is 6. Since 2 + 2 + 2 is 6, triangle is 2. In the second example, square plus 2 is 10, so square is 10 – 2, or 8.

Mystery Numbers 4

1 4

2 1

3 Answers will vary. In the second example, triangle plus triangle plus 2 is 10, so triangle plus triangle is 10 – 2, or 8. Since the double 4 + 4 is 8, triangle is 4. In the first example, square plus 4 is 5, so square is 5 – 4, or 1.

Mystery Numbers 5

1 5

2 10

3 Answers will vary. In the first example, square plus square plus square is 15. Since 5 + 5 + 5 is 15, square is 5. In the second example, triangle minus 5 is 5, so triangle is 5 + 5, or 10.

Mystery Numbers 6

1 9

2 4

3 Answers will vary. If square plus triangle is 13 in the second example, then square plus triangle is also 13 in the first example. Replace the square and one triangle in the first example with 13. That leaves 13 plus triangle equal to 22. Thus, triangle is 9. Then in the second equation, square plus 9 is 13, so square is 13 – 9, or 4. Students may use guess and check strategies to find the answers.

Across and Down 1

Same shapes are same numbers.

Add across.

Add down.

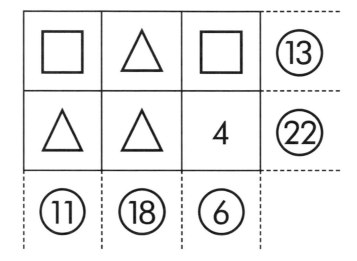

Numbers in ◯ are sums.

1 What number is ☐? _____

2 What number is △? _____

3 Explain how you found the numbers. _____

_____

Across and Down 1

Solutions
p 72

Goals

Replace variables with numbers.

Identify relationships between variables and numbers.

Questions to Ask

What do you see in the second row? (2 triangles and the number 4.)

What does the number 22 at the end of the second row mean? (It is the sum of 2 triangles and the number 4.)

What does the number 6 at the bottom of the third column mean? (It is the sum of square and 4.)

What number does square stand for? (2) *Why?* (Because 2 + 4 is 6.)

Solutions

1 2

2 9

3 Answers will vary. Since the third column shows that square plus 4 is 6, then square is 6 − 4, or 2. The second column shows that 2 triangles are 18. That means that triangle is half of 18, or 9.

Students should verify their answers by writing the numbers in the shapes and checking the sums for each row and column.

First row: 2 + 9 + 2 = 13

Second row: 9 + 9 + 4 = 22

First column: 2 + 9 = 11

Second column: 9 + 9 = 18

Third column: 2 + 4 = 6

Notes

In this problem set, some students may have difficulty with the grid format. Talk about the five sums within the grid (two horizontal, three vertical). You may want to ask students to write or tell all five sums before they start.

Across and Down 2

Same shapes are same numbers.

Add across.

Add down.

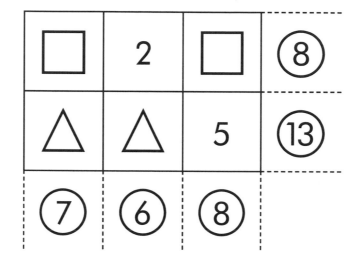

Numbers in ◯ are sums.

1 What number is ☐ ? _____

2 What number is △ ? _____

3 Explain how you found the numbers. _____

_____

Across and Down 3

Same shapes are same numbers.

Add across.

Add down.

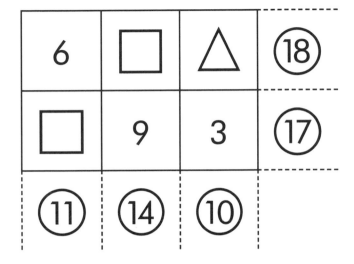

Numbers in ◯ are sums.

1 What number is ▢ ? _____

2 What number is △ ? _____

3 Explain how you found the numbers. _____

_____

★ ★ ★ ★

Across and Down 4

Same shapes are same numbers.

Add across.

Add down.

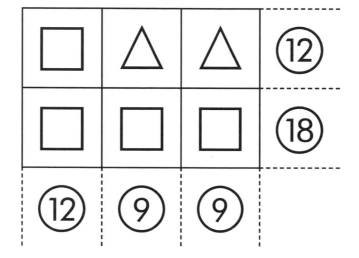

Numbers in ◯ are sums.

1 What number is ☐? _____

2 What number is △? _____

3 Explain how you found the numbers. _____

_____

VARIABLE • ACROSS AND DOWN

Across and Down 5

Same shapes are same numbers.

Add across.

Add down.

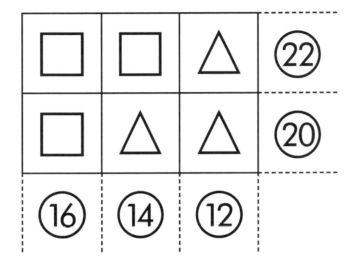

Numbers in ⃝ are sums.

1 What number is ☐ ? _____

2 What number is △ ? _____

3 Explain how you found the numbers. _____

_____

GROUNDWORKS 77

VARIABLE • ACROSS AND DOWN

Across and Down 6

Same shapes are same numbers.

Add across.

Add down.

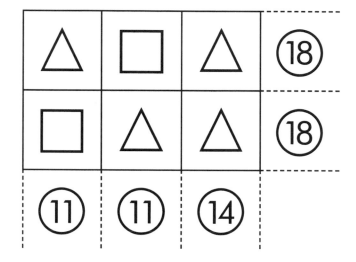

Numbers in ◯ are sums.

1 What number is ☐ ? _____

2 What number is △ ? _____

3 Explain how you found the numbers. _____

_____

SOLUTIONS • Variable • Across and Down

Across and Down 2

1 3

2 4

3 Answers will vary. Since the third column shows that square plus 5 is 8, then square is 8 – 5, or 3. The second column shows that 2 plus triangle is 6. That means that triangle is 6 – 2, or 4.

Across and Down 3

1 5

2 7

3 Answers will vary. Since the second column shows that the square plus 9 is 14, then square is 14 – 9, or 5. The third column shows that triangle plus 3 is 10. That means that triangle is 10 – 3, or 7.

Across and Down 4

1 6

2 3

3 Answers will vary. The first column shows that square plus square is 12. Since 6 + 6 is 12, square is 6. The second column, then, shows that 6 plus triangle is 9, so triangle is 9 – 6, or 3.

Across and Down 5

1 8

2 6

3 Answers will vary. Since the first column shows that square plus square is 16, and 8 + 8 is 16, then square is 8. The second column shows that 8 plus triangle is 14, so triangle is 14 – 8, or 6.

Across and Down 6

1 4

2 7

3 Answers will vary. Since the third column shows that triangle plus triangle is 14, and 7 + 7 is 14, then triangle is 7. The second column shows that square plus 7 is 11, so square is 11 – 7, or 4.

VARIABLE • ACROSS AND DOWN

Weighing Blocks 1

Same shapes weigh the same.

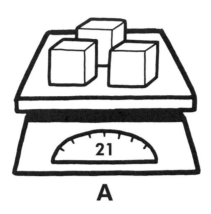

A

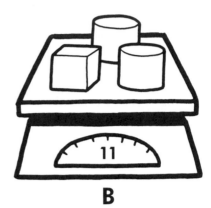

B

1 ⬜ weighs _____ pounds.

2 ⬛ weighs _____ pounds.

3 How did you find the the weight of ⬛ ? _____

_____

_____

**Solutions
p 80**

Weighing Blocks 1

Goals

Replace pictures with numbers.

Identify weights of blocks from relationships shown symbolically.

Questions to Ask

How many pounds does Scale A show? (21 pounds)

What do you see on Scale A? (3 cubes)

How much does one cube weigh? (7 pounds)

How do you know? (Since 3 cubes weigh 21 pounds, and 7 + 7 + 7 = 21, 1 cube weighs 7 pounds.)

How much do the 2 cylinders weigh on Scale B? (4 pounds. Since one cube weighs 7 pounds, then the two cylinders weigh 11 − 7, or 4 pounds.)

Solutions

1 7

2 2

3 On Scale A, one cube weighs 7 pounds. On Scale B, the cube and 2 cylinders weigh 11 pounds. Replacing the cube with 7, the 2 cylinders weigh 11 − 7, or 4 pounds. Then 1 cylinder weighs half of 4, or 2 pounds.

Notes

Suggest to students that they find the scale that will be the most helpful to use first. It will not always be Scale A.

☆ ☆

Weighing Blocks 2

Same shapes weigh the same.

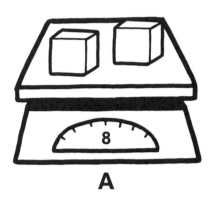

A

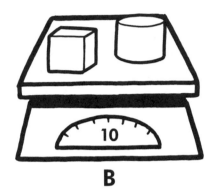

B

1 ⬜ weighs _____ pounds.

2 ⬭ weighs _____ pounds.

3 How did you find the the weight of ⬭ ? _____

_____

_____

Weighing Blocks 3

Same shapes weigh the same.

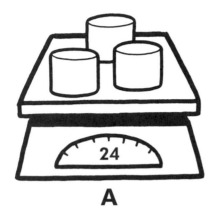 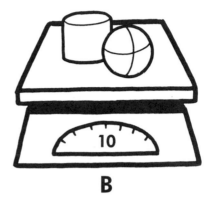

A **B**

1 ⊕ weighs _____ pounds.

2 ⬭ weighs _____ pounds.

3 How did you find the the weight of ⊕ ? _____

_____

_____

Weighing Blocks 4

Same shapes weigh the same.

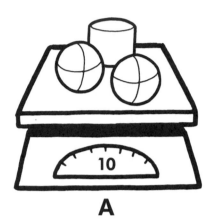

A

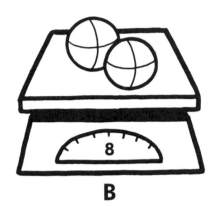

B

1 ⊕ weighs _____ pounds.

2 ⬭ weighs _____ pounds.

3 How did you find the the weight of ⬭ ? _____

_____

_____

Weighing Blocks 5

Same shapes weigh the same.

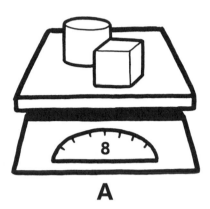

A

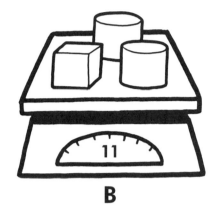

B

1 ⬜ weighs _____ pounds.

2 ⬭ weighs _____ pounds.

3 How did you find the the weight of ⬭ ? _____

_____

_____

☆ ☆ ☆ ☆ ☆ ☆

Weighing Blocks 6

Same shapes weigh the same.

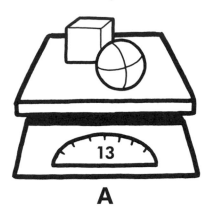

A

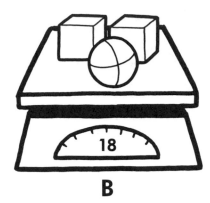

B

1 ⬜ weighs _____ pounds.

2 ⊕ weighs _____ pounds.

3 How did you find the the weight of ⊕? _____

_____

SOLUTIONS • Variable • Weighing Blocks

Solutions
pp 82–86

Weighing Blocks 2

1 4

2 6

3 On Scale A, 2 cubes weigh 8 pounds. Since cube plus cube is 8 pounds, and 4 + 4 is 8, one cube weighs 4 pounds. Replace the cube on Scale B with 4 pounds. Thus, the cylinder weighs 10 – 4, or 6 pounds.

Weighing Blocks 3

1 2

2 8

3 On Scale A, 3 cylinders weigh 24 pounds. Since cylinder plus cylinder plus cylinder is 24 pounds, and 8 + 8 + 8 is 24, one cylinder weighs 8 pounds. Replace the cylinder in Scale B with 8 pounds. Thus, the sphere weighs 10 – 8, or 2 pounds.

Weighing Blocks 4

1 4

2 2

3 On Scale B, 2 spheres weigh 8 pounds. Since sphere plus sphere is 8 pounds, and 4 + 4 is 8, one sphere weighs 4 pounds. Replace the 2 spheres on Scale B with 8 pounds. Thus, the cylinder weighs 10 – 8, or 2 pounds.

Weighing Blocks 5

1 5

2 3

3 Since 1 cylinder and 1 cube together weigh 8 pounds on Scale A, replace 1 cylinder and 1 cube with 8 pounds on Scale B. Thus, the extra cylinder on Scale B weighs 11 – 8, or 3 pounds. On Scale A, replace the cylinder with 3 pounds. Thus, the cube weighs 8 – 3, or 5 pounds.

Weighing Blocks 6

1 5

2 8

3 Since 1 sphere and 1 cube together weigh 13 pounds on Scale A, replace 1 sphere and 1 cube with 13 pounds on Scale B. Thus, the extra cube on Scale B weighs 18 – 13, or 5 pounds. On Scale A, replace the cube with 5 pounds. Thus, the sphere weighs 13 – 5, or 8 pounds.

Mystery Machines 1

15 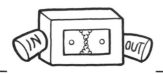 5   40 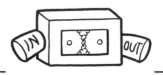 30

1 Tell what comes out.   **2** Tell what comes out.

12 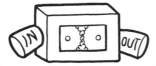 ____   36 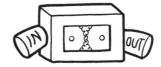 ____

3 Tell what comes out.   **4** Tell what comes out.

80 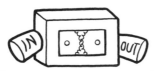 ____   127 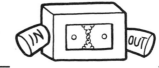 ____

5 Tell what goes in.   **6** Tell what goes in.

____ 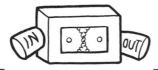 18   ____ 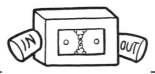 41

7 Tell what goes in.   **8** Tell what goes in.

____ 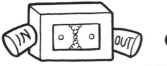 90   ____  200

9 Write what the 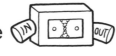 does to the numbers that go in.

_____

Mystery Machines 1

Solutions
p 88

Goals

Deduce the function rule from the examples.

Apply the function rule to determine the output when given the input.

Apply the function rule to determine the input when given the output.

Write a rule that tells what the machine does.

Questions to Ask

What number went into the first machine? (15)

What number came out of the first machine? (5)

What number went into the second machine? (40)

What number came out of the second machine? (30)

What is the same about the two numbers that came out? (They are each 10 less than the number that went in.)

Solutions

1	2	**2**	26
3	70	**4**	117
5	28	**6**	51
7	100	**8**	210

9 The machine subtracts 10 from the number that goes in.

Notes

In this problem set, there are always two completed examples to help students figure out the operations of the machine. Students may want to write the operation in or under the machine to help them realize the answer, rather than determine it mentally.

Mystery Machines 2

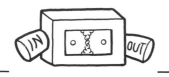 5 ____ 16   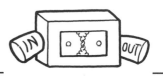 28 ____ 39

1 Tell what comes out.   **2** Tell what comes out.

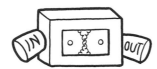 4 ____   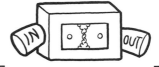 10 ____

3 Tell what comes out.   **4** Tell what comes out.

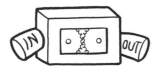 0 ____   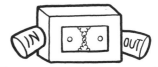 54 ____

5 Tell what goes in.   **6** Tell what goes in.

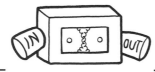 ____ 13   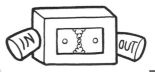 ____ 25

7 Tell what goes in.   **8** Tell what goes in.

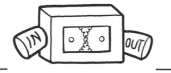 ____ 46   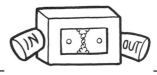 ____ 91

9 Write what the 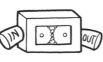 does to the numbers that go in.

_____

Mystery Machines 3

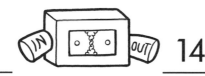 42   142

 100   200

1 Tell what comes out.

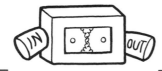 2   _____

2 Tell what comes out.

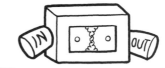 50   _____

3 Tell what comes out.

 95   _____

4 Tell what comes out.

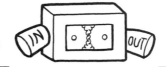 300   _____

5 Tell what goes in.

 _____ 106

6 Tell what goes in.

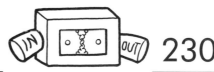 _____ 230

7 Tell what goes in.

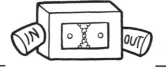 _____ 471

8 Tell what goes in.

 _____ 900

9 Write what the 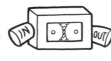 does to the numbers that go in.

_____

Mystery Machines 4

14 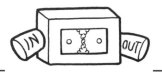 2   27 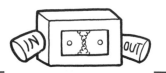 15

1 Tell what comes out.

15 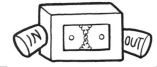 _____

2 Tell what comes out.

19 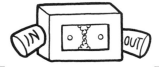 _____

3 Tell what comes out.

12 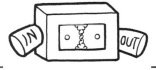 _____

4 Tell what comes out.

25 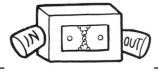 _____

5 Tell what goes in.

_____  5

6 Tell what goes in.

_____ 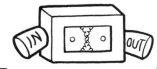 12

7 Tell what goes in.

_____ 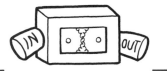 4

8 Tell what goes in.

_____ 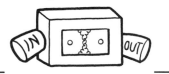 10

9 Write what the does to the numbers that go in.

_____

Mystery Machines 5

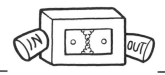 2 ____ 4

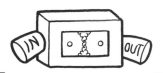 6 ____ 12

1 Tell what comes out.

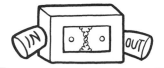 3 ____

2 Tell what comes out.

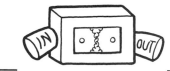 11 ____

3 Tell what comes out.

 8 ____

4 Tell what comes out.

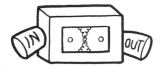 7 ____

5 Tell what goes in.

 ____ 10

6 Tell what goes in.

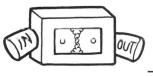 ____ 24

7 Tell what goes in.

 ____ 18

8 Tell what goes in.

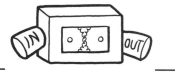 ____ 6

9 Write what the 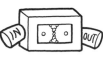 does to the numbers that go in.

_____

Mystery Machines 6

2 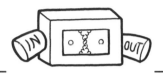 6   5 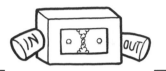 15

1 Tell what comes out.

3 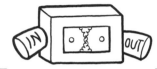 _____

2 Tell what comes out.

6 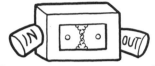 _____

3 Tell what comes out.

10  _____

4 Tell what comes out.

7 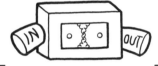 _____

5 Tell what goes in.

_____ 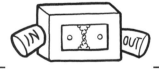 12

6 Tell what goes in.

_____ 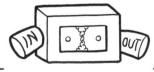 24

7 Tell what goes in.

_____ 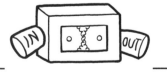 36

8 Tell what goes in.

_____ 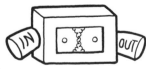 27

9 Write what the 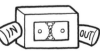 does to the numbers that go in.

_____

SOLUTIONS • Function • Mystery Machines

Solutions pp 90–94

Mystery Machines 2

1 15

2 21

3 11

4 65

5 2

6 14

7 35

8 80

9 The machine adds 11 to the number that goes in.

Mystery Machines 3

1 102

2 150

3 195

4 400

5 6

6 130

7 371

8 800

9 The machine adds 100 to the number that goes in.

Mystery Machines 4

1 3

2 7

3 0

4 13

5 17

6 24

7 16

8 22

9 The machine subtracts 12 from the number that goes in.

Mystery Machines 5

1 6

2 22

3 16

4 14

5 5

6 12

7 9

8 3

9 The machine doubles (multiplies by 2) the number that goes in.

Mystery Machines 6

1 9

2 18

3 30

4 21

5 4

6 8

7 12

8 9

9 The machine triples (multiplies by 3) the number that goes in.

Two-Steppers 1

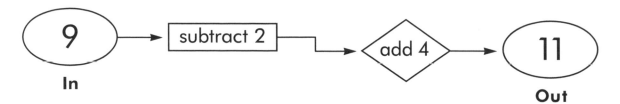

In 9 → subtract 2 → add 4 → 11 **Out**

What comes out?

1 8 → subtract 2 → add 4 → ⬭

2 26 → subtract 2 → add 4 → ⬭

What goes in?

3 ⬭ → subtract 2 → add 4 → 7

4 ⬭ → subtract 2 → add 4 → 40

5 Use → ⬡ → for → subtract 2 → add 4 → .

20 → ⬡ → 22

Explain what ⬡ does. _____

_____

Two-Steppers 1

Solutions
p 96

Goals

Follow and complete sequences of computations.

Apply function rules to determine the output when given the input.

Apply function rules to determine the input when given the output.

Write a rule to describe a function.

Questions to Ask

What number goes into the stepper first? (9)

What does the first part of the stepper do the number? (It subtracts 2.)

What number would be the result after the first step? (7)

What does the second part of the stepper do to that number? (It adds 4.)

What is the final result? (11)

Solutions

1 10

2 28

3 5

4 38

5 The hexagon adds 2 to the "In" number. The hexagon replaces the two steps "subtract 2 then add 4."

Notes

In this problem set, the "What goes in?" section is especially interesting. You can observe students' understanding of the reversibility of operations. Do students use a strategy of guess and check, or do they "undo" the operations from right to left to get the answers?

Two-Steppers 2

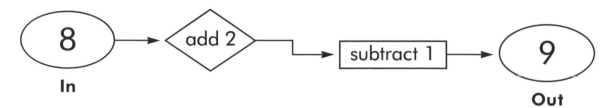

8
In → add 2 → subtract 1 → 9 **Out**

What comes out?

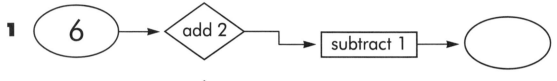

1 6 → add 2 → subtract 1 → ⬭

2 15 → add 2 → subtract 1 → ⬭

What goes in?

3 ⬭ → add 2 → subtract 1 → 3

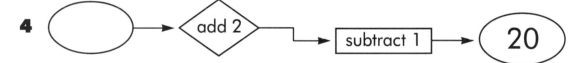

4 ⬭ → add 2 → subtract 1 → 20

5 Use ⬡ for → add 2 → subtract 1 → .

15 → ⬡ → 16

Explain what ⬡ does. _____

_____

Two-Steppers 3

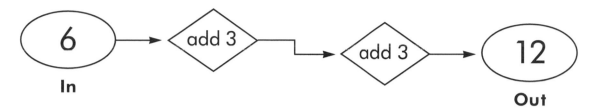

In → add 3 → add 3 → **Out**

What comes out?

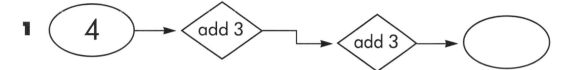

1 4 → add 3 → add 3 →

2 23 → add 3 → add 3 →

What goes in?

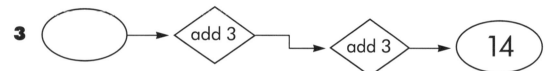

3 → add 3 → add 3 → 14

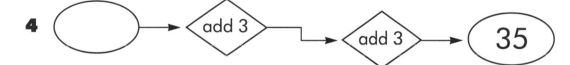

4 → add 3 → add 3 → 35

5 Use → ⬡ → for → add 3 → add 3 → .

16 → ⬡ → 22

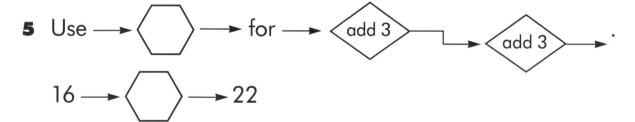

Explain what ⬡ does. _____

_____

GROUNDWORKS 99

Two-Steppers 4

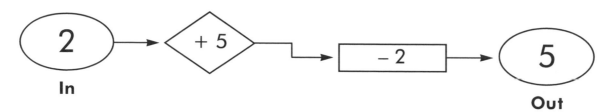

What comes out?

1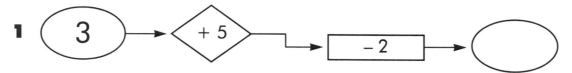

2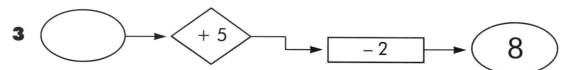

What goes in?

3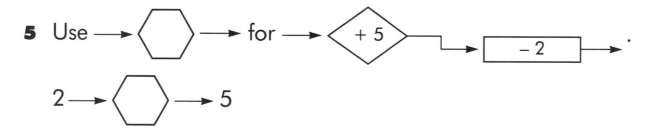

4

5 Use ⬡ for +5 ─2 .

2 ⬡ 5

Explain what ⬡ does. _____

_____

Two-Steppers 5

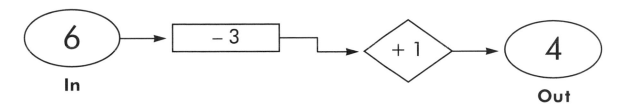

In

Out

What comes out?

1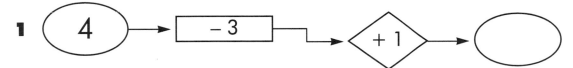

2 (12) → [− 3] → ⟨ + 1 ⟩ → ( )

What goes in?

3 ( ) → [− 3] → ⟨ + 1 ⟩ → (8)

4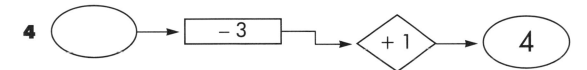

5 Use → ⬡ → for → [− 3] → ⟨ + 1 ⟩ → .

5 → ⬡ → 3

Explain what ⬡ does. _____

_____

Two-Steppers 6

$$10 \xrightarrow{\text{In}} \boxed{-4} \rightarrow \boxed{-4} \rightarrow 2 \text{ Out}$$

What comes out?

1 $\quad 12 \rightarrow \boxed{-4} \rightarrow \boxed{-4} \rightarrow \bigcirc$

2 $\quad 24 \rightarrow \boxed{-4} \rightarrow \boxed{-4} \rightarrow \bigcirc$

What goes in?

3 $\quad \bigcirc \rightarrow \boxed{-4} \rightarrow \boxed{-4} \rightarrow 3$

4 $\quad \bigcirc \rightarrow \boxed{-4} \rightarrow \boxed{-4} \rightarrow 10$

5 Use $\longrightarrow \hexagon \longrightarrow$ for $\longrightarrow \boxed{-4} \rightarrow \boxed{-4} \rightarrow$.

$13 \longrightarrow \hexagon \longrightarrow 5$

Explain what $\hexagon$ does. _____

_____

Solutions
pp 98–102

Two-Steppers 2

1 7

2 16

3 2

4 19

5 The hexagon adds 1 to the "In" number. The hexagon replaces the two steps "add 2 then subtract 1."

Two-Steppers 3

1 10

2 29

3 8

4 29

5 The hexagon adds 6 to the "In" number. The hexagon replaces the two steps "add 3 then add 3."

Two-Steppers 4

1 6

2 15

3 5

4 1

5 The hexagon adds 3 to the "In" number. The hexagon replaces the two steps "add 5 then subtract 2."

Two-Steppers 5

1 2

2 10

3 10

4 6

5 The hexagon subtracts 2 from the "In" number. The hexagon replaces the two steps "subtract 3 then add 1."

Two-Steppers 6

1 4

2 16

3 11

4 18

5 The hexagon subtracts 8 from the "In" number. The hexagon replaces the two steps "subtract 4 then subtract 4."

Number Patterns 1

1 This is a **+9** number pattern. Complete the pattern.

1, 10, 19, 28, 37, _____, _____, _____

+9 +9

2 This is a **−7** number pattern. Complete the pattern.

40, 33, 26, _____, _____, _____

−7 −7

3 Complete the pattern.

4, 14, 24, 34, _____, _____, _____

4 What kind of pattern is this?_____

5 Make a **+** number pattern.

Start with 8.

Give the first 6 numbers. _____

6 Make a **−** number pattern.

Start with 50.

Give the first 6 numbers. _____

INDUCTIVE REASONING • NUMBER PATTERNS

Number Patterns 1

Solutions p 104

Goals

Identify and continue number patterns.

Create addition and subtraction number sequences.

Questions to Ask

What is the first number in the first pattern? (1) *What is the second number?* (10)

What do you do to get from the first number to the second number? (Add 9.)

Do you do the same thing to get from the second number to the third number? third to fourth?
   fourth to fifth? (Yes, add 9.)

What is the number after 37? (46) *How do you know?* (37 + 9 = 46)

What is the next number in the second pattern? (19)

Solutions

1 46, 55, 64

2 19, 12, 5

3 44, 54, 64

4 +10 pattern

5 Answers will vary. Be sure that the addition pattern begins with 8 and the same number is added each time. It should have 6 terms.

6 Answers will vary. Be sure that the subtraction pattern begins with 50 and the same number is subtracted each time. It should have 6 terms.

Notes

In this problem set, all patterns involve either adding or subtracting a number repeatedly. You can extend the "make your own pattern" questions by giving students a start number and an end number, and asking them if they can find a pattern that gets them from start to end in two, three, or any specified number of steps.

Number Patterns 2

1 This is a **+2** number pattern. Complete the pattern.

3, 5, 7, 9, 11, _____, _____, _____
  +2   +2

2 This is a **−1** number pattern. Complete the pattern.

20, 19, 18, _____, 16, _____, _____
  −1   −1

3 Complete the pattern.

50, 45, 40, 35, 30, _____, _____, _____

4 What kind of pattern is this? _____

5 Make a **+8** number pattern. Give the first 6 numbers.

_____

6 Make a **−8** number pattern. Give the first 6 numbers.

_____

INDUCTIVE REASONING • NUMBER PATTERNS

Number Patterns 3

1 This is a **+6** number pattern. Complete the pattern.

1, 7, 13, 19, 25, _____, _____, _____

+6 +6

2 This is a **−4** number pattern. Complete the pattern.

30, 26, 22, _____, _____, 10, _____, _____

−4 −4

3 Complete the pattern.

3, 7, 11, 15, _____, _____, _____

4 What kind of pattern is this?_____

5 Make a **+3** number pattern. Give the first 6 numbers.

_____

6 Make a **−2** number pattern. Give the first 6 numbers.

_____

Number Patterns 4

1 This is a **+5** number pattern. Complete the pattern.

1, 6, 11, 16, 21, _____, _____, _____

+5 +5

2 This is a **–3** number pattern. Complete the pattern.

30, 27, 24, _____, _____, 15, _____, _____

–3 –3

3 Complete the pattern.

2, 5, 8, 11, 14, _____, _____, _____

4 What kind of pattern is this? _____

5 Make a **+** number pattern. Give the first 6 numbers.

_____

6 Make a **–** number pattern. Give the first 6 numbers.

_____

INDUCTIVE REASONING • NUMBER PATTERNS

Number Patterns 5

1 This is a **+10** number pattern. Complete the pattern.

4, 14, 24, 34, 44, _____, _____, _____
+10 +10

2 This is a **−5** number pattern. Complete the pattern.

90, 85, 80, _____, 70, _____, _____
−5 −5

3 Complete the pattern.

7, 12, 17, 22, 27, _____, _____, _____

4 What kind of pattern is this?_____

5 Make a **+** number pattern.

Start with 5.

Give the first 6 numbers. _____

6 Make a **−** number pattern.

Start with 25.

Give the first 6 numbers. _____

Number Patterns 6

1 This is a **+8** number pattern. Complete the pattern.

2, 10, 18, 26, 34, _____, _____, _____
+8   +8

2 This is a **−6** number pattern. Complete the pattern.

40, 34, 28, _____, 16, _____, _____
−6   −6

3 Complete the pattern.

5, 12, 19, 26, 33, _____, _____, _____

4 What kind of pattern is this?_____

5 Make a **+** number pattern so that the second number is 8. Give

the first 6 numbers. _____

6 Make a **−** number pattern so that the second number is 40. Give

the first 6 numbers. _____

Solutions
pp 106–110

Number Patterns 2

1 13, 15, 17

2 17, 15, 14

3 25, 20, 15

4 − 5 pattern

5 Answers will vary. Be sure that the addition pattern adds 8 each time and has 6 terms.

6 Answers will vary. Be sure that the subtraction pattern subtracts 8 each time and has 6 terms.

Number Patterns 3

1 31, 37, 43

2 18, 14, 6, 2

3 19, 23, 27

4 + 4 pattern

5 Answers will vary. Be sure that the addition pattern adds 3 each time and has 6 terms.

6 Answers will vary. Be sure that the subtraction pattern subtracts 2 each time and has 6 terms.

Number Patterns 4

1 26, 31, 36

2 21, 18, 12, 9

3 17, 20, 23

4 + 3 pattern

5 Answers will vary. Be sure that the addition pattern adds the same number each time and has 6 terms.

6 Answers will vary. Be sure that the subtraction pattern subtracts the same number each time and has 6 terms.

Number Patterns 5

1 54, 64, 74

2 75, 65, 60

3 32, 37, 42

4 + 5 pattern

5 Answers will vary. Be sure that the addition pattern begins with 5, adds the same number each time, and has 6 terms.

6 Answers will vary. Be sure that the subtraction pattern begins with 25, subtracts the same number each time, and has 6 terms.

Number Patterns 6

1 42, 50, 58

2 22, 10, 4

3 40, 47, 54

4 + 7 pattern

5 Answers will vary. Be sure that the addition pattern adds the same number each time, that the second number is 8, and has 6 terms.

6 Answers will vary. Be sure that the subtraction pattern subtracts the same number each time, that the second term is 40, and has 6 terms.

Square Patterns 1

Design 1   **Design 2**   **Design 3**   **Design 4**

The pattern continues.

How many in

1 Design 5? _____

2 Design 7? _____

3 Design 10? _____

How many ■ in

4 Design 5? _____

5 Design 7? _____

6 Design 10? _____

7 Which design has 12 □? _____

8 Which design has 15 ■? _____

INDUCTIVE REASONING • SQUARE PATTERNS

Square Patterns 1

Solutions
p 112

Goals

Identify patterns.

Continue patterns to identify numbers of elements.

Questions to Ask

How many unshaded squares in Design 1? (2) *in Design 2?* (3) *in Design 3?* (4) *in Design 4?* (5)

How many unshaded squares will be in Design 5? (6)

Why do you think so? (The number of unshaded squares is always one more than the design number.)

How many shaded squares in Design 1? (0) *in Design 2?* (1) *in Design 3?* (2) *in Design 4?* (3)

How many shaded squares will be in Design 5? (4)

Why do you think so? (The number of shaded squares is always one fewer than the design number.)

How many more unshaded squares than shaded squares are in Design 3? (2) *in Design 4?* (2) *in Design 5?* (2)

Solutions

1	6	**2**	8
3	11	**4**	4
5	6	**6**	9
7	Design 11	**8**	Design 16

Notes

In this problem set, students identify a rule for the pattern. They then must use that rule to figure out the answers to the questions. Some students may need extra paper to sketch the patterns.

Square Patterns 2

Design 1

Design 2

Design 3

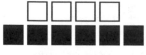
Design 4

The pattern continues.

How many ☐ in

1 Design 5? _____

2 Design 6? _____

3 Design 10? _____

How many ■ in

4 Design 5? _____

5 Design 6? _____

6 Design 10? _____

7 Which design has 11 ☐? _____

8 Which design has 14 ■? _____

Square Patterns 3

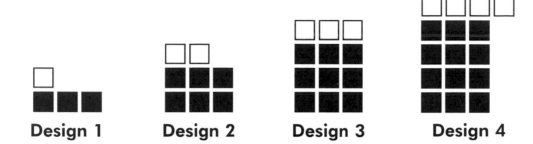

Design 1   **Design 2**   **Design 3**   **Design 4**

The pattern continues.

How many ☐ in

1 Design 5?_____

2 Design 6?_____

3 Design 8?_____

How many ■ in

4 Design 5?_____

5 Design 6?_____

6 Design 8?_____

7 Which design has 15 ☐? _____

8 Which design has 30 ■? _____

Square Patterns 4

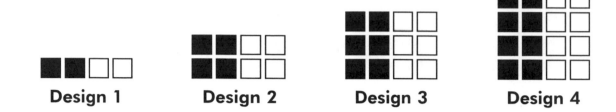

Design 1 **Design 2** **Design 3** **Design 4**

The pattern continues.

How many ☐ in

1 Design 5? _____

2 Design 8? _____

3 Design 10? _____

How many ■ in

4 Design 5? _____

5 Design 8? _____

6 Design 10? _____

7 Which design has 18 ☐? _____

8 Which design has 24 ■? _____

Square Patterns 5

Design 1 **Design 2** **Design 3** **Design 4**

The pattern continues.

How many ☐ in

1 Design 5? _____

2 Design 7? _____

3 Design 10? _____

How many ■ in

4 Design 5? _____

5 Design 7? _____

6 Design 10? _____

7 Which design has 14 ☐? _____

8 Which design has 34 ■? _____

Square Patterns 6

☐☐   ☐☐☐☐   ☐☐☐☐☐☐   ☐☐☐☐☐☐☐☐
                   ■   ■■   ■■■

Design 1   **Design 2**   **Design 3**   **Design 4**

The pattern continues.

How many ☐ in

1 Design 5? _____

2 Design 7? _____

3 Design 10? _____

How many ■ in

4 Design 5? _____

5 Design 7? _____

6 Design 10? _____

7 Which design has 14 ☐? _____

8 Which design has 17 ■? _____

Solutions
pp 114–118

Square Patterns 2

1 5

2 6

3 10

4 7

5 8

6 12

7 Design 11

8 Design 12

Square Patterns 4

1 10

2 16

3 20

4 10

5 16

6 20

7 Design 9

8 Design 12

Square Patterns 6

1 10

2 14

3 20

4 4

5 6

6 9

7 Design 7

8 Design 18

Square Patterns 3

1 5

2 6

3 8

4 15

5 18

6 24

7 Design 15

8 Design 10

Square Patterns 5

1 6

2 8

3 11

4 10

5 14

6 20

7 Design 13

8 Design 17

Bibliography

Commission on Standards for School Mathematics of the National Council of Teachers of Mathematics. *Curriculum and Evaluation Standards for School Mathematics.* Reston, VA: National Council of Teachers of Mathematics, 1989.

Greenes, Carole, and Carol Findell. *Algebra: Puzzles and Problems.* Chicago: Creative Publications, 1998.

Secretary's Commission on Achieving Necessary Skills. *What Work Requires of Schools.* SCANS Report of America 2000. Washington D.C.: U.S. Department of Labor, 1991.

Standards 2000 Writing Group. *Principles and Standards for School Mathematics: Discussion Draft.* Reston, VA: National Council of Teachers of Mathematics, 1998.

About the Authors

Carole Greenes is a Professor of Mathematics Education at Boston University. She is the author of numerous mathematics books and programs for students from pre-K through grade twelve. She is a member of the management team for the Boston University-Chelsea Project and works regularly with students in the Chelsea schools to help them acquire and apply big ideas in mathematics. Dr. Greenes is currently a member of the College Board's Equity 2000 committee and the Algebra Assessment development team. She is also chairperson of the task force charged with rewriting the Mathematics Framework for the state of Massachusetts.

Carol Findell is an Associate Professor of Mathematics Education at Boston University. She works regularly with teachers and aspiring teachers of mathematics at all levels of education. Dr. Findell is particularly interested in problem solving, and has written problems for Student Math Notes and two of the annual World's Largest Math Events, which were sponsored by the National Council of Teachers of Mathematics. She is currently chairperson of the writing team for the MathCounts competitions.